My Friends

by Nick Sharratt & Stephen Tucker

Oxford University Press

We've brought bread
for the ducks to eat,
They all say thank you
for their treat.
Quack! Quack! Quack!

The tiny baby's fast asleep,
tucked up in her cot.
If we go and wake her up
she'll cry, so better not.
Shhhh!

This dog is friendly,
Very big, too.
It's going to lick me!
What shall I do?

I thought I'd call to say 'Hello.'

Bye-bye for now, I've got to go.

How many fishes in the tank,
Are there three or four?
It's hard to count when
        they swim about,
That's why I'm not sure.

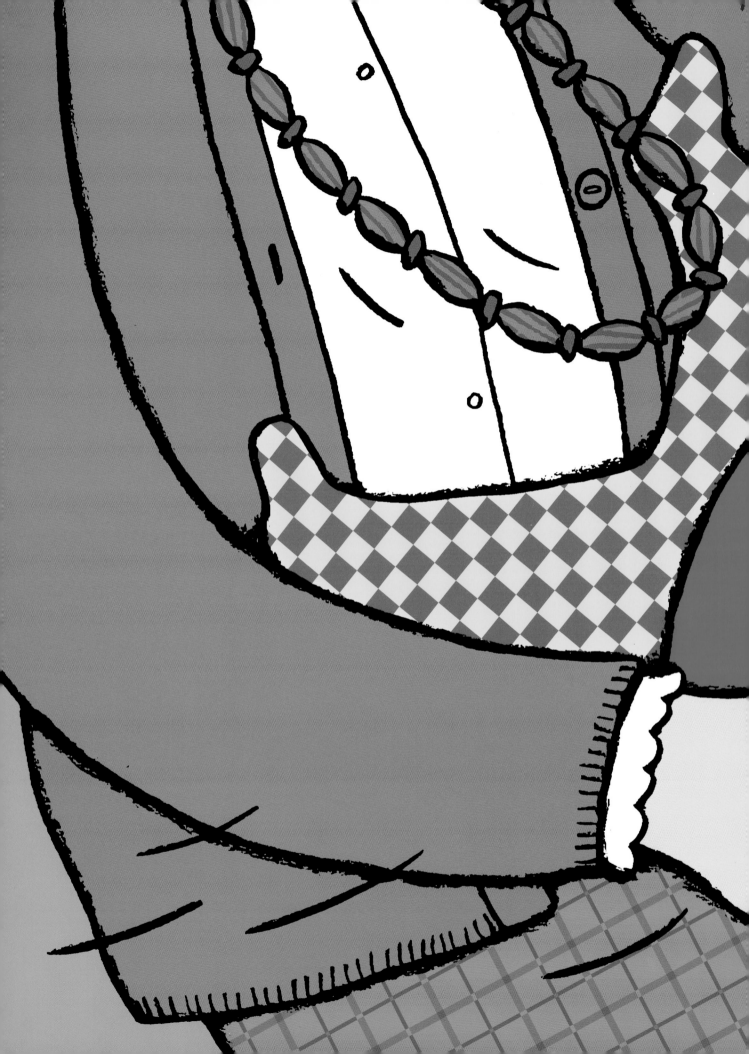

Lift me off the ground
And whirl me round
and round!

Say goodnight to Rabbit,
Say goodnight to Ted,
Say goodnight to Woolly Lamb
And snuggle down in bed.